One BOY, One STONE, One GOD

The Story of David
and Goliath for children
1 Samuel 17

Written by Michelle Medlock Adams
Illustrated by Steven James Petruccio

CONCORDIA PUBLISHING HOUSE · SAINT LOUIS

Young David watched his father's sheep;
he cared for every lamb.
He worshiped God and played his harp.
He loved the Great I Am.

"Dear son, come here," said David's dad.
"I have a job for you."
"Okay," said David to his dad.
"Just tell me what to do."

"Please take this roasted grain and cheese
and these ten loaves of bread.
Your brothers and the other men
are needing to be fed.

"They're warring with the Philistines;
you'll find them over there.
Please find out how they're doing, son,
and let them know we care."

When finally he reached the camp,
both armies stood their ground.
He heard the war cry loud and clear—
it was a scary sound!

"Hey, brothers!" David called ahead.
"Our father sent me here.
He's worried over each of you.
His heart is full of fear."

Just then a booming voice rang out.
It sounded loud and gruff.
The voice came from a nine-foot man.
He acted really tough.

Goliath was this giant's name.
He mocked each Israelite.
He challenged every one of them
to come on out and fight.

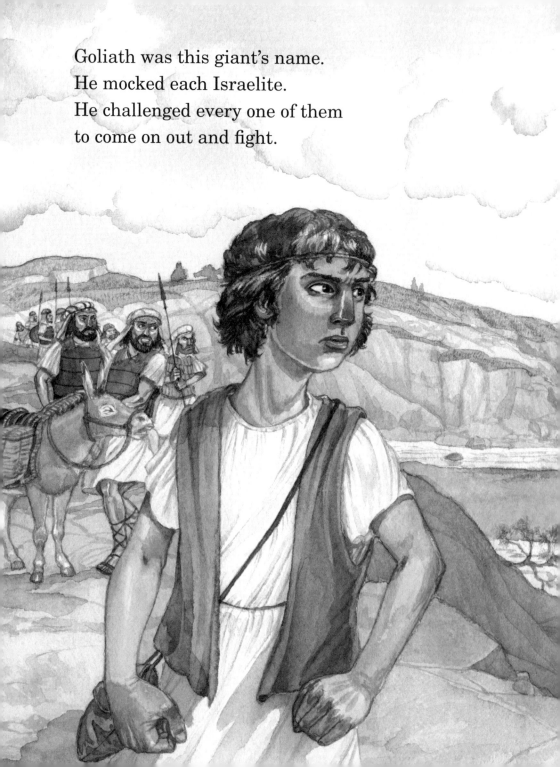

Young David watched the Philistine.
He listened to his words:
"Whoever tries to conquer me—
I'll feed him to the birds."

His words made David really mad;
he longed to fight the man.
I'll beat that giant, David thought.
With God, I know I can.

When Saul got news of David's words,
he said, "You're just a lad.
This man's been fighting all his life.
He's big and mean and bad!"

"But I can do it," David said.
"The Lord will help me win.
He's helped me kill wild animals.
He'll help me once again."

"Okay," said Saul. "Well, go ahead.
I trust the things you've said.
Here, take my coat of armor, boy,
and helmet for your head."

"I cannot wear these,"
David said.
"They do not fit at all."
He took the coat of armor off
and gave it back to Saul.

So David went down to the stream.
He dug down in the sand.
And, one by one, he found five stones.
He clenched them in his hand.

Then, David stood and grabbed his sling
and headed for the fight.
The giant mocked and laughed at him
and cursed him left and right.

"You come at me with sword and spear,"
said David to the man.
"But I come in the name of God!"
Then all at once, he ran.

He charged right at the Philistine.
The giant charged right back.
Then David flung a little stone
and started his attack.

The stone moved swiftly through the air
and struck the giant's head.
That's when it happened—*Boom! Kersplat!*
The giant fell down dead!

The Philistines were very scared.
They all began to run.
With sling and stone and God's great hand,
The battle had been won!

Though David wasn't very old,
God knew what he could do.
God used him in a mighty way,
and God will use you too!

DEAR PARENTS,

The story of David and Goliath is one of the best-known Bible stories to children. It celebrates success for the little guy and hope for those who are threatened by an enemy. We love stories like this. The idea of standing up to a bully inspires courage.

We face giants every day: terrifying, larger-than-life giants such as war and oppression and cancer, as well as those that don't look that much bigger than we are, like a late car payment or difficulties at work. But the most threatening giant in every life is sin. Sin mocks us and laughs at us; it slings arrows of accusations until we want to run and hide.

We are like those Israelite soldiers, cowering hopelessly as sin and Satan wage war with us. We are also like King Saul, taking up shields and swords of our own making in our attempt to fight sin on our own. Ultimately, we are saved not by anything we do but by one man who did battle for us—Jesus Christ.

There are many layers and many lessons in this Bible story. But the one that is most important for your child now is that it is God's power that arms us with all we need to face the giants in our lives. With faith in the Word of God, and wrapped in the robe of Christ's righteousness, we can be sure that Jesus has defeated sin and we need not fear it.

When you read this book with your child, talk about the things that scare him or tempt him. Perhaps there's a bully at school or a behavior to change. Just like David, we can be confident that Jesus is our ultimate source of strength in all things. Faith in Him and His power will strengthen us to confront those giants, no matter what they are.

The Editor